SIPPS

S0-AAB-686

Extension Level

STORY BOOK

A project of Developmental Studies Center.

Published by Developmental Studies Center, Oakland, CA
and Scholastic Inc., New York, NY.

Note to the teacher:

The pages of this Story Book can be used as reproducible masters for take-home stories. Their illustrations are designed to photocopy in black and white. Permission is granted for reproduction for educational purposes only.

ISBN 0-439-35788-8

Printed in the U.S.A.

1 2 3 4 5 6 7 8 9 10   8   08 07 06 05 04 03 02 01

Co-published by
Developmental Studies Center
2000 Embarcadero, Suite 305
Oakland, CA 94606
and
Scholastic Inc.
555 Broadway
New York, NY 10012.

CONTENTS

Lesson 1

The Helping Dog
Chapter 1   Ron and Lab

Ron is a man. He can not see. He has a dog to help him. The dog is a Lab. Ron calls him Lab.

When Ron has to go out, he puts straps on Lab.

The straps are on Lab's chest and his back and under him.

Ron gets Lab's little rug into his pack and zips it up. He picks up his pack. He puts Lab's straps in his left hand. Then he tells Lab to go.

As they go, Lab helps Ron. When Lab goes, Ron will go. When Lab stops, Ron will stop. If Lab sees a box in the way, he will help Ron go by the box. Lab gets Ron out of the way so Ron will not trip.

When Lab sees a dog, he will not run. He will not sniff. He will not play with the dog. He will stay by Ron.

Lesson 2

The Helping Dog
Chapter 2   To Ron's Job

Lab helps Ron go to his job. They have to cross to the bus stop. If a truck comes, Lab stops fast. He will not let Ron go on. When the truck goes by, then Lab lets Ron go.

They get to the bus stop. When the bus comes, they step up into the bus. Ron sits down at the front. Lab sits next to him.

A man on the bus tells Ron when to get off. When they come to Ron's stop, Lab helps Ron step down off the bus.

Then they go on to Ron's job. Ron sits down at his desk. He gets the little rug from his pack. He puts it down flat. Lab has a nap on the rug by Ron's desk.

Lab helps Ron go to lunch and then back to his job. At last Ron can go. Ron checks Lab's straps. Then they go back on the bus.

Lesson 3

The Helping Dog
Chapter 3   Lab Can Play

Lab and Ron are back from Ron's job. Ron puts down his pack and gets the straps off Lab.

Then Ron gets Lab his dish. Yum! Lab licks his dish. Then he gets a drink.

"You can play," says Ron.

Lab has a sock which he likes to tug on with Ron. He is strong. He will not let go. When Ron gets the sock, Lab grabs it from Ron's hand.

Then Lab sits on Ron's lap. Ron says, "You are my Lab on a lap! You are the best dog! I can trust you, and you are fun!" Ron hugs Lab.

Ron says, "Stand still." Ron brushes Lab with a dog brush. He pats him.

Then Ron goes to bed. He has Lab's rug next to his bed. Lab stretches and then rests on the rug.

When Lab helps Ron see, Lab is not a pet, but when he plays with Ron, he is a pet.

Lesson 4

The Smelling Test

Sniff was the class pet. The class fed Sniff and played with him. Sniff was a rat.

Why was he called Sniff? He liked to smell things. Rats can smell things we can't smell. When the class let him out, he went under all the desks sniffing.

The class had a plan to test Sniff's smelling. They hid a bit of lunch in a bag. They put the bag in a can with no top. They put the can in a big box. They put the box at the end of a long shelf. They added little boxes on the shelf and put a ramp from a little box up to the big box. Then they lifted Sniff up to the shelf.

Sniff smelled that lunch. He passed the little boxes, went up the ramp, and got into the big box. He went in the can and got into the bag. Here was his lunch. He sat up on his back legs and bit into it.

The class said Sniff did well on his smelling test.

11

Lesson 5

The Bug's Trip

A little bug wished to see what was going on in class. So with a little buzz, he went in.

He landed on a shelf. The class was doing math.

"Well, well," said the bug, "I will go to a desk."

He buzzed down to Jane's desk. She was quick at math. She liked math.

Then the bug went to Bill's desk.

"No, Bill, no," said the bug. "Six plus six is not ten. Check it, check it."

Then he buzzed to Mac. Mac was not adding. Mac was thinking of P.E. He was thinking of pitching and catching. He was thinking, "We will win. I will get lots of hits and runs."

"Do math, Mac. Quit thinking of P.E." said the bug.

On to Ling's desk. She had her hand up to ask for help. She was humming, too.

"This is fun," said the bug. "What is next? Here is the class frog." The bug saw its strong legs. He saw the frog jump from rock to rock in its box.

Just then Jane said, "The frog can have his lunch."

"Lunch for the frog?" said the bug. "Not me! Class was fun but I must go! Fast!"

13

Lesson 6

The Story of Cat
Chapter 1   The Gate and Some Cake

Jane and Rick had an old cat that was black and white. This cat had no name. They just called her "Cat."

There was no other cat in the home. So when Jane said, "Cat, come here!" Cat came running to her. When Rick called, "Here, Cat," Cat came to him.

But if the sun was up, Cat did not come when her name was called. Cat did not like to sit on the bed in her home. She did like to sit outside. Cat sat and sat in the sun for a long time. Jane asked Rick, "Why does Cat like sunshine so much?" Rick said, "Cat is old. I think she is cold."

Cat sat on the gate by the side of her home. She sat in the same spot every time. Cat did not chase rats. Cat did not like to chase a snake. She would just sit on the gate in the hot sun.

But Cat did like one other thing. She did like cake. When Jane called, "Cat, here is some cake!" Cat would jump up and run into her home. Jane said, "Cat, you like the taste of cake. You like to lick cake. You like to get cake on your nose and on your white legs."

Lesson 7

The Story of Cat
Chapter 2   Cat's Game

Cat did not chase rats. She did not like to play with balls of string. Cat just sat on the gate outside her home.

Cat did one other thing. It was something that dogs like to do. A dog likes to run and get things and bring them back. If you toss a ball in the grass, a dog will get it and drop it next to you. If you toss a big stick into a lake, dogs will swim to get it and will bring it back to shore.

Cat did not like to chase balls. She did not like to get sticks in a lake. Cat did not like to swim at all! But she did like to get the plastic tops of milk jugs. It was a game. Jane played this game with Cat many times.

Jane would toss the milk top on the rug in her home. Cat would run to the plastic cap and jump on it. She would then bring it back to Jane.

Over and over they played the same game. Sometimes Cat would hide the plastic cap. She would not bring it back to Jane. Cat would hide it in a pile of socks by the bed. When Jane could not find it, the game ended. Cat would go back outside and sit on the gate.

Lesson 8

The Story of Cat
Chapter 3   Cat Wants a Kitten

One time, Rick kept some of his cake for Cat. He called, "Cat, where are you hiding? Come and get some cake. I am saving it just for you. I am taking it to your dish. It has white frosting on top. You can lick it and get it all over your black nose and on your white legs."

But this time Cat did not come running. She was sitting on the gate. Cat was looking at a mother cat with a kitten. These two cats were white and black. The mother cat was chasing her kitten. Then the kitten was chasing his mother. The game looked like fun. In a while, the mother cat and her kitten stopped to rest. The mother licked her kitten. The kitten's chin was on his mother's leg.

Cat was sad. She felt very sad. She wanted a kitten to lick. She wanted to go chasing it all over the grass.

Rick saw Cat looking at the two cats. He said, "Cat, you want a kitten to play with but you are an old cat. Kittens are a big job. Come here and get some cake."

Cat jumped off the gate and came in to get the cake. She did not walk very fast. The sun was shining but she was sad.

19

Lesson 9

The Story of Cat
Chapter 4   Still Sad

Rick told Jane that Cat was sad. Jane asked, "Why is Cat sad?"

Rick said, "She saw a mother cat playing with her kitten. The mother chased the kitten and the kitten chased its mother. Then, the mother licked her kitten. The kitten liked it a lot. I think Cat wants a kitten to take care of. But she is too old to have kittens. What can we do to help Cat? I gave her some cake when I came in. Cat ate the cake but she is still sad."

Jane said, "I have a plan. Let's get her to fetch the plastic top off a milk jug. She likes that game. I hope we can find the plastic top. Cat hid it the last time we played the game of fetch."

Rick and Jane went looking for a plastic milk top.
They looked in Cat's bed. No top. They looked in Cat's
dish. No top. They looked in a pile of old socks. A top!
There it was. It was inside a red and black sock. There
was a big hole in the side of the sock.

Jane tossed the top on the rug. Cat chased it and
came back to Jane. Jane tossed the top one more time.
This time Cat did not chase it. Cat went outside. She
was still sad.

Lesson 10

The Story of Cat
Chapter 5   Cat's Doll

Jane called out, "Wake up, Cat. It's time to get up. It is time to run outside. You can jump up on the gate and sit in the sun. You can watch me ride my bike."

Cat got out of her bed and walked outside. She jumped up on the gate. A large black bug ran up her chin. Cat licked her chin, and the bug fell off. Cat sniffed the large bug but did not step on it. The black bug ran down the gate. Rick came by and waved at Cat.

Just then the sun went in back of Cat's home. The sun stopped shining on Cat. She was in the shade. Cat didn't like sitting in the shade. So she went back inside.

After lunch, Rick and Jane saw Cat with Jane's stuffed doll. It was a little doll with a red hat and a pink dress. Cat grabbed the doll and walked to her basket. She sat in her basket and licked the doll. Cat licked the doll's legs. She licked her red hat. She licked her pink dress. Then she put her chin on the doll's leg.

"What is Cat doing with that doll?" Jane asked.

Rick said, "Cat thinks the doll is her kitten. She is acting as if it is her kitten.

Lesson 11

The Story of Cat
Chapter 6   The Bike Ride

Rick and Jane wanted to go on a bike ride after school. Mom and Dad were going to walk with them. Rick wanted to take a snack. He put a peach and ten green beans in a sack. (Green beans? Yes, some children like to eat green beans for a snack.) Jane was still full from lunch. She did not feel like eating. Rick had a lot of things in the basket on his bike. There was his snack, three balls, and nine trucks. The basket was very full.

When they got to a steep hill, Rick had to get off and push his bike. "Why did I bring all this stuff?" Rick asked. Mom helped pull his bike. Rick stopped to rest. Dad put a rock in back of the wheel to keep the bike from going back. Rick ate his peach and three green beans.

Just then, Jane saw a basket by the side of the street. She walked over and looked inside. There were two kittens sleeping on a pile of rags! There was a note next to the kittens. The note said, "Free to a good home."

Jane asked, "What does the note mean?"

Dad said, "It means you can take the kittens home but you must take good care of them."

Lesson 12

The Story of Cat
Chapter 7 "Can We Keep Them?"

Rick asked, "Why would someone want to give these kittens up? They are so cute. They look very clean."

Mom said, "I will read the back of the note. It says:

I have sixteen cats. I cannot take care of any more.
These kittens are six weeks old. They can eat meat.
The vet gave them all their shots.
Their tags are on their necks.

Jane said, "We could give the kittens a good home. Why can't we keep them? We can feed them meat and fish. Rick and I will take good care of them every week."

Mom asked, "We have Cat. Do we need more cats?"

Rick said, "I think Cat needs a kitten to take care of and play with. They can play hide and seek. They can all sleep in the same basket. They can lick each other clean."

Dad and Mom said, "OK. The kittens can live with us. Cat does want a kitten. We think you will feed them."

They all went home. Rick and Jane rode their bikes. Dad had to carry the basket of kittens for a mile. Just before they got home, the kittens woke up and looked out of the basket. Cat was on the gate. She saw the kittens.

Mom said, "Cat, you wanted a kitten. We have two!"

Lesson 13

The Story of Cat
Chapter 8   What Will Cat Do?

Would Cat like the kittens? Would she want to hurt them? Some cats will hurt the kittens of other cats. Dad walked to the gate. He was still carrying the basket of kittens. They were sitting up. Everyone watched Cat.

At first, Cat got up on her feet and turned to look at the kittens. Then she hissed. The kittens saw Cat's teeth. One kitten jumped out of the basket and landed in the dirt. The other kitten jumped on Dad's shirt and then fell on Dad's feet. Cat jumped off the gate and walked over to the kittens. Cat hissed one more time. Then Cat stopped hissing. She moved closer and sniffed each kitten. Then she licked them. First she licked the fur of one kitten. Then she licked the fur of the other kitten. The kittens purred and purred. They felt safe.

"Well," said Jane. "I think Cat loves them. If she did not like them, she would not lick their fur. I am so glad. When Cat is done, those kittens will have very clean fur."

Rick said, "It's time to feed the kittens. I will get some milk for them to drink and some meat to eat. Most kittens like milk and meat. Cake is not good for kittens!"

Lesson 14

The Story of Cat
Chapter 9   The Best Cat Names

Mom said, "The kittens ate most of the meat. The milk is all gone. Those kittens sure need to eat a lot."

When the kittens were done eating, they felt like playing. First they ran in the dirt. Then they ran after a bird. But the bird flew up into a tree. One kitten did catch a little bug. But the bug curled up into a little ball. The other kitten ran under a green fern. (A fern is a plant.) Cat watched them and purred. She was not a sad cat.

Dad said, "What will we call the kittens? We need to think of two good names. One kitten is a male and one is a female. What are the best names for our new pets?"

Everyone came up with a few names: "White Feet, Black Nose, Soft Fur, Big Chin, Flat Back, Cat Nip, Cat Sup, Sup Per, Din Ner." These were not the best names.

Jane said, "Look! The kittens are playing a new game. It looks like 'catch me if you can.' They are taking turns chasing each other. First they run here. Then they go there. Turn here. Turn back. Look at them zigzag."

"That's it!" said Rick. "Let's call them Zig and Zag. Zig and Zag like to zigzag in the grass and in the dirt."

Lesson 15

The Firefighters

Chapter 1   The Fire Bell Rings

Rose was a firefighter. In that job you have to be ready all the time. When a call for help comes in, you have to move fast.

One time the fire bell rang when Rose and the other firefighters were eating lunch. They had to leave their lunch.

Rose pulled on her turn-outs. Turn-outs are thick clothes with wide stripes that shine in the dark. Her turn-outs and hard hat help keep her safe from fire, heat, and falling sparks.

Rose got a print-out telling her where the fire was. She ran to the truck, got in, and started the truck.

Her friends were running to the other trucks. The ladder truck is so long that two people must drive, one in the front cab, and one in the back cab. Vic drove in the front. Lee sat in the back cab. He steered by turning the rear wheels.

Rose drove fast but she watched the streets. When cars hear the fire trucks and see them flashing, they must move to the side while the fire trucks pass.

Rose was asking herself, "What will this fire be like?"

Far off she saw black smoke. As they got near, she saw the red flames rising.

Lesson 16

The Firefighters

Chapter 2   Fire at a Store

This time the fire was at a store. With horns honking the trucks rushed into the parking lot.

The firefighters pulled the hoses off the trucks and set them up. Rose started to pump the water.

Vic and Lee put the ladder up and went to the top of the store. They cut holes to let the heat out.

Jack and Pat had to check to see if people were still inside the burning store. They put on smoke masks and wore tanks with tubes for breathing. They walked into the store. It was dark and full of smoke. Inside they did find two very scared people. Pat and Jack led them out.

When a fire seems to be out, it can still be burning in some parts of the walls. Jack felt for warm spots on the walls. Then he chopped holes with his ax to look for more fire.

At last the fire was out. Pat set up large fans to clear the smoke out of the store.

Everyone lifted up the hoses to let the water run out. They put the hoses back on the truck.

Two firefighters were left near the store to watch for more fire, but it did not start up again.

Lesson 17

The Firefighters

Chapter 3   Back From the Fire

The firefighters rode back from the fire. Rose backed the truck in. She parked it so she would not have to back out for the next fire. Backing out takes too much time.

They felt tired, but they could not stop to rest yet. First they had to clean up to be ready for the next call.

They checked the first aid kit. They got the used air tanks off the truck and put on full ones.

Jack cleaned the smoke and dirt off of the ax and fans. Vic and Lee put clean spare hoses on the truck.

At last they could rest.

"We did a great job today," said Rose.

"Let's eat," said Lee.

"It's your turn to make the meal," said Vic.

Lee and Rose fixed pork, beef, and other meat. They heated up greens, corn, and peas. They served beans and cheese in a large dish. The meal was ready, and everyone sat down. After all that work, they like to eat!

Then they watched TV and played games. When bedtime came, they put their turn-out pants next to their beds. If the fire bell rang again, they would wake up, pull their pants on fast, and run to the trucks.

Lesson 18

The Firefighters
Chapter 4   Clean Up Again

The firefighters had work to do each day.

Lee and Vic kept the fire truck clean and neat. They squirted it with water and scrubbed the dirt off. They cleaned the wheels and tires. Vic was the one who liked to make the truck shine. He rubbed the water off with a cloth.

"No water spots on this truck!" said Vic with pride.

Rose and Jack did the hard part of cleaning up. The hoses they used at the fire had a lot of dirt and smoke on them. If dirt is left on the hoses for a long time, the dirt will rub the hoses and make holes in them. Then the water will leak out.

The hoses were very long and hard to lift. First Rose and Jack stretched them out and laid them next to each other. They sprayed water on top and brushed the dirt off with a large brush.

Then they turned all the hoses over and brushed the other side. They sprayed the hoses again. Then they lifted the hoses on to racks. Hoses will dry in one or two days.

When will the next call come in? The firefighters are ready! They are brave. They like helping people. They like their work.